Writing Springboards

Lottie Kent

Year 5

Springboards

HOPSCOTCH EDUCATIONAL PUBLISHING

Published by
Hopscotch Educational Publishing Ltd,
Unit 2, The Old Brushworks, 56 Pickwick Road,
Corsham, Wiltshire SN13 9BX
Tel: 01249 701701

© 2004 Hopscotch Educational Publishing

Written by Lottie Kent
Series design by Blade Communications
Illustrated by Lottie Kent
Printed by cle-print

ISBN 1-904307-65-5

Contents

Introduction

About the series

Writing Springboards is an innovative series of books aimed at developing and enriching the writing skills of children at Key Stage 2. The activities are matched to the National Literacy Strategy's *Framework for Teaching* for Years 3 to 6 but the activities could easily be used with older or younger children.

There are four books in the series: Year 3, Year 4, Year 5 and Year 6.

Each book aims to:
* support teachers by providing a wealth of interesting ideas for writing lessons;
* reduce teachers' preparation time through the provision of photocopiable resources;
* stimulate children's interest and enjoyment in writing;
* develop and enhance children's writing skills through stimulating and purposeful activities that are fun to do.

Written and illustrated by a practising teacher, the activities have been trialled in schools with outstanding success. The ideas are fresh and exciting and guidance is provided to enable teachers to use the same activity in a variety of different ways.

About each book

Each book contains 15 units of work, specifically written to cover the range of text level work outlined in the *Literacy Framework* for each year group. Where appropriate to the activity, there are also some sentence level objectives included. The activities can be used throughout the school year, enabling the teacher to focus on developing appropriate skills in fiction, poetry and non-fiction writing for each term.

Each unit consists of four photocopiable sheets plus teacher's notes that provide lots of practical ideas and suggestions for how the sheets can be used.

The three photocopiable activity sheets can be used for differentiated tasks for specific children or groups during a lesson, or within a series of literacy lessons where the children may work as a whole class, in groups or individually. Where particular children need support, the sheets can be used to prepare them for a writing activity, giving them more confidence to contribute their ideas. They are also an ideal way to motivate the more reluctant writers in a class. The activities will inspire children's creativity and add sparkle to any lesson!

The fourth photocopiable sheet contains just the main illustration and this can be used in a variety of ways:
* as a stimulus for writing assessment;
* for generating the teacher's own questions as an introduction to the writing task;
* as a starting point for a writing activity in a different genre;
* to use in discussion, developing the children's skills in speaking and listening;
* for the teacher to make it into a word bank to support specific children;
* for SEN support – working on a child's particular literacy targets

At the back of the book are some extra sheets that can be used to support any of the units.

Response partners sheet
This can be used to encourage children to work with others to evaluate their work and make decisions about possible improvements to their writing.

Self-assessment sheet
This can be used to help focus the writer on assessing the key aspects of their writing and evaluate their success.

Writing targets sheet
This can be used to help pupils to concentrate on areas for improvement.

Publishing and display ideas sheets
These sheets can be used by both the teacher and the children themselves to provide them with lots of exciting ideas for publishing and displaying their writing.

Unit 1 – The bus stop

Learning objectives

- To write own playscript, including production notes (Term 1, T18).
- To create characters for a play.
- To annotate a playscript in preparation for performance (Term 1, T19).

Ideas for using the activity sheets

Page 6: The bus stop

- Look at the setting for the scene. Discuss how the sheet is set out as production notes and explain that it would include the set design, lighting and sound. Ask the children to work in pairs to write down the production notes for the scene. Tell them to share their ideas – have they included enough/too much detail?
- Look at examples of play scenes and discuss how they build up. Are all the characters on stage at the beginning/end of the scene? The children could work in small groups planning the stage directions and lines for the start of the scene. They could perform it to the class.
- Decide on a plot for the play. What could be happening? Is there a problem? Ask the children to work in small groups, planning the plot as a group. Once decided, the group could work together on the lines for each character. Perform the scenes and compare their ideas.

Page 7: Bus stop – characters

- Watch part of a television drama. Discuss what sort of character each actor is portraying. How can we tell? The children could write a detailed description of one of the characters on the sheet.
- Discuss the need to develop each character's personality in order to make them believable. Complete the sheet as a class, scribing their ideas. The children could then work in pairs, practising taking on the role of one character. At the end, the class could ask each child, in role, questions about themselves. Can they guess which character they are playing?
- The children could introduce another character to the scene. Tell them to build up a description of the character, including notes about how they will affect the scene. They could practise playing the new part and, at the end, introduce themselves to the rest of the class as the new character. The class could make comments about the new person. What sort of person are they?

Page 8: Bus stop – conversations

- Discuss the type of conversation the children on the scene could have. Would they use slang? Nicknames? Gestures? Ask the children to work in pairs to develop the conversation between the two characters, including stage directions. Encourage them to write their ideas in rough and practise them, making changes where necessary.
- Bring three pairs together, with their written conversations. Act as a director with the help of the class. Build up a script for the whole scene, including stage directions, production notes, props and so on. Adapt the ideas as the scene progresses, using suggestions from the class. The children could perform the finished piece to another class.
- Develop their ideas in the next scene of the play. Ask them to write and practise the new scene as a small group, and to share the performance with the rest of the class.

The bus stop

Make notes around the picture.

Give each character a name.

When is it?

Where is it set?

Describe the setting.

What are they doing?

What sounds can you hear?

What props are needed?

What is the problem?

How would the scene start?

How would the scene end?

Decide the order in which they would appear on the set.

Bus stop – characters

Choose one character from each picture to write about.

Name:

What does he/she look like?

What is he/she like?

What is his/her mood?

Name:

What does he/she look like?

What is he/she like?

What is his/her mood?

Name:

What does he/she look like?

What is he/she like?

What is his/her mood?

Bus stop – conversations

What are they talking about?

How are they speaking?

Names?

Are there pauses?

Are they friends?

How are they feeling?

Are there any actions?

Choose two of the characters from the picture and write
a conversation between them. Use the prompts to help.

Setting

Characters

Scene

Unit 2 – The trip

Learning objectives

- To write different story openings (Term 1, T1).
- To write new scenes or characters into a story (Term 1, T15).
- To map out text, showing development and structure (Term 1, T14).

Ideas for using the activity sheets

Page 11: The trip

- Look at the differences between writing in the 1st and 3rd person. Ask the children to use a completed sheet to write about the scene in the 1st person. Then ask them to swap pieces of writing with a partner and rewrite someone else's work in the 3rd person. Ask them to share the changes with their partner.
- Look at a familiar story. Discuss the stages of the story and where the high and low points are. As a class, look at the picture and map out a story plan with the scene at the beginning. Recognise high and low points in the plan. The children could then work in small groups to develop different story plans with the scene at different stages.
- Look at how writing is organised in paragraphs. Complete the sheet as whole class (OHT) and use the ideas to plan what information would be included in consecutive paragraphs. The children could use the plan to write a series of paragraphs about the scene. Read and compare their finished paragraphs.

Page 12: The trip – characters

- Look at examples of characters in stories. Discuss how they are presented through dialogue, action and description. How does the author want the reader to respond to that character? Look at one of the characters on the sheet as a whole class. Act as a scribe, writing about the character in different ways to portray his/her personality. The children could write about a different character, choosing a personality type for them and deciding how to present them (dialogue, action or description).
- Discuss the children's own experiences of trips. Make a list of words to describe their feelings. How did they prepare themselves? Did they get up early for the trip? How did they feel afterwards? They could write a diary page for the day of their trip and then write another one for one of the characters on the sheet.
- Ask the children to introduce another character to the scene. Discuss who this person could be and how they would fit in with the rest of the characters. What impact would they have? Ask the children to use the sheet to write about the new character and write a conversation between him/her and one of the other characters.

Page 13: The trip – opening

- Look at different story openings. Discuss which they prefer and why. Decide the different ways stories can be started and ask the children to work in pairs to write the start to the story in three different ways.
- Look at how dialogue can be used to start a story. Discuss the difference between direct and reported speech (model the two types). The children could write a story opening, using direct speech and then reported speech. Ask them to share the two extracts and discuss which they prefer and why.
- The children could act out the scene as a playscript. They could practise in small groups and write a script for it (including stage directions) and then perform it to the class.

The trip

Make notes around the picture.

Where are they going?

How will they get there?

What are they taking with them?

What will happen?

What sort of day is it?

When is it?

Where is it?

Who are they?

How do they know each other?

How are they feeling?

The trip - characters

Write what each character
is saying or thinking.

Choose one of the characters to write about.

What do they look like?

What are they wearing?

What do they like to do?

How are they feeling?

What sort of person are they?

The trip – opening

Write three different openings to the story.

You could start with:

Dialogue Action Description

Character's thoughts

Unit 3 – The playground

Learning objectives

- To convey feelings, moods in a poem through word choice (Term 1, T16).
- To write metaphors from original ideas or from similes (Term 1, T17).
- To use different styles and structures from poems read.

Ideas for using the activity sheets

Page 16: The playground

- Read various poems about schools. Discuss common themes and make a collection of words and phrases used. Look at the structure of one poem and identify the rhyming pattern and so on. Scribe a verse for a playground poem using this structure. The children could work in pairs to continue the poem.
- Look at different rhyming patterns in poetry and discuss their impact. Use ideas on completed sheets to experiment with different rhyming patterns. Together, identify the basic content for the lines in the first verse. Ask the children to work in pairs to try different patterns, experimenting with words and word order. Share their most successful ideas. They could then go on to write further verses.
- In small groups, the children could focus on collecting ideas on one aspect of the picture (for example, sounds or feelings). They could develop lines on that particular theme. Share each group's ideas and scribe a whole class poem.

Page 17: Playground feelings

- Discuss the feelings you have when there isn't anyone to play with. Ask the children to share their experiences. List words to describe that feeling. Ask the children to use the completed sheet to write a poem that really reflects that mood.
- Discuss the variety of emotions on the playground (happy, angry and scared). The children could work in pairs, writing a poem reflecting a particular mood/emotion. They should use the questions on the sheet as prompts for their ideas. Share the finished poems and discuss which words/lines really portray that feeling.
- Look at examples of similes and metaphors. Recognise the difference and look at how each is used, for impact, in poetry. Discuss what the child on the sheet might compare the playground to. Ask the children to use ideas on the sheet to write a series of metaphors to show the character's feelings. They could then reorganise these lines into a poem.

Page 18: Playground verses

- Challenge the children to work in small groups to make their verses rhyme. They need to consider which rhyming pattern they wish to adopt and try out different ideas in draft form. They then make a final draft that they all agree on as the best. They could read out their poems to the class, discuss the most successful parts and identify the rhyming patterns.
- Discuss what a playground can be compared to; for example, a battlefield, funfair or jungle. Choose one comparison and model how the poem could be completed using metaphors. The children could choose another comparison and complete the poem using suitable metaphors.
- Ask the children to develop the ideas into a performance poem. Ask them to make up a chorus, including actions and sound effects. They could perform the poem in small groups to the class.

The playground

Make notes around the picture.

What can you see?

What sounds can you hear?

What is the weather like?

What are they doing?

How do they feel?

What are they saying?

Playground feelings

Imagine you are this person.

Answer the questions to reflect your mood.

How are you feeling?

Why are you sitting alone?

Where are your friends?

Where would you rather be?

What can you hear?

What are some of the children doing? How does it make you feel?

What is playtime like for you?

Playground verses

Think about these when composing your verses:

Similes

Metaphors

Moods/feelings

Rhyming patterns

Interesting vocabulary

Rhythm

The playground was ....

Children ....

Sound of ....

Everywhere ....

The playground was ....

Friends ....

Feeling ....

All about ....

Can you make it rhyme?

Now, read through your verses.

Does it keep to a rhythm?

Are there better words?

Is the word order good?

Unit 4 – The parcel

Learning objectives

- To write recounts for different audiences (Term 1, T 24).
- To use the features of recounted texts (Term 1, T 24).
- To use appropriate layout for a recount text (Term 1, T 24).

Ideas for using the activity sheets

Page 21: The parcel

- Look at different types of recount. Identify which are formal/informal styles and how they are written with different audiences in mind. Complete the sheet on an OHT as a class. Ask the children to use the information to write a recount in a style of their choice. Share their finished pieces and look at differences/similarities.
- The children could use the information on the sheet to write a recount as a letter to a friend telling them about the parcel. Model how the letter should be set out and where certain information should go.
- Would the postal worker have to write a report on the incident with the parcel? Discuss what sort of information she would have to include. Work as a class devising a report form. The children could then work in pairs, completing the report.
- Focus on the chronological sequence. Make a list of suitable time connectives that will help. The children could use the details on the sheet to write a sequence of sentences using the connectives.

Page 22: The parcel report

- Look at examples of newspaper reports and discuss the main features. Highlight these features on the examples and display a reminder of the key points. The children could work in pairs writing a report on the story pictured.
- Look at recounts of the same story in tabloid papers and broadsheets. Compare the language used. Model writing the report for a broadsheet. Ask the children to rewrite the report for a tabloid paper. Read and compare.
- Look at the importance of headlines in newspaper reports. Investigate different methods used; for example, alliteration, play on words. The children could work with computers, devising suitable headlines for the story.

Page 23: My parcel

- Ask the children to work together in pairs, using an empty box to role play receiving their parcel. Their partner asks the questions and records the answers on the sheet. They could use the answers to write a recount.
- Look at examples of diary pages. Discuss how this type of recount differs from others. Ask the children to write a diary entry for the day they received the parcel. This could then be developed for the the following days, when they did something with the parcel.
- Ask the class to imagine that they are police officers called to the scene of a theft. The contents of the box have been stolen. The parcel belonged to their teacher. Decide what was in the box and then model answering the questions about it for the whole class. The children could write a police report recounting the incident.

The parcel

Make notes around the picture.

Where is it?

When is it?

Who are they?

What are they going to do?

Why have they sent it?

What is happening?

What is in the parcel?

Where has it come from?

Who has sent it?

Who is it for?

┌───┐
│   │
│   │
└───┘

Reported by

(catchy headline)

(orientation)

....

....

....

....

....

....

(caption)

(main events)

....

....

....

....

....

....

....

....

(reorientation)

....

....

....

My parcel

What is in your parcel? Draw it inside the box and then answer the questions about it.

Where were you when it arrived?

When did you receive it?

How did you react to it?

What are you going to do?

What is it?

Is it valuable?

Where has it come from?

Why did they send it to you?

Who has sent it to you?

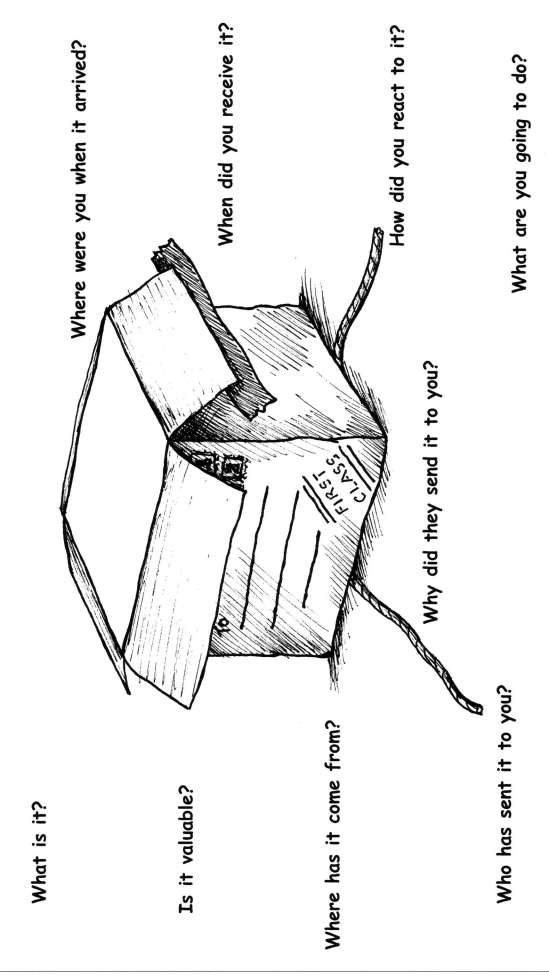

Unit 5 – Basketball

Learning objectives

- To write instructional texts and test them out (Term 1, T25).
- To use verbs in the imperative in instructional writing (Term 1, S9)
- To use the features of instructional texts (Term 1, T25).

Ideas for using the activity sheets

Page 26: Basketball

- Ask the children to work in small groups, collecting information about basketball from different sources (internet, books, organisations) in order to answer the questions. Discuss which sources were the most useful. Were there any questions they couldn't answer?
- Invite a player/coach to talk to the class about the sport. Use the sheet to generate questions.
- Ask the children to use the completed sheet to design a poster about basketball. Discuss the use of illustrations to make certain things clear. They could work in pairs, designing a poster on general information and rules. Display their finished work and evaluate their effectiveness.

Page 27: Basketball rules

- Play a game of basketball. The children should take it in turns to make notes about the game while acting as spectators. Share their notes with the class. Use their ideas to scribe a plan for their instructions. Complete the sheet using the plan.
- Look at written rules for different games. In small groups, the children could evaluate how useful and easy to use they are (record comments). Share the comments with the whole class. Ask the children to consider the comments when completing the sheet.
- Look at the use of verbs in the imperative. Locate their use in instructional texts. Model writing a series of sentences as an explanation of how to play basketball. The children could change them into instructions by using verbs in the imperative. Compare their finished instructions.

Page 28: Rules for …

- The children could work in small groups, discussing the rules for their chosen game. They could then work individually on the rules for one aspect of the game; for example, passes, fouls and scoring. The group could then bring all the sheets together to make a rules booklet for the sport.
- Look at playtime games. Ask the children to write the rules for games they play. Use the playground to try out the games, and check that the rules are clear and include enough information. They could swap games with other groups and evaluate them. Make laminated copies of the games for children to use at playtimes.
- Look at different types of games and make a class list. Think about equipment used, where it can be played, physical or mental games, number of players and so on. Ask the children to make up the rules for a new game based on one of the types listed. Try out the game – does it work? Is it fun? Ask another class to try out the games.

Basketball

Make notes around the picture.

What equipment do you need?

Where would you play?

How many are in a team?

How long is a match?

What are the passes called?

Are there fouls?

Are there words/phrases associated with the game?

Any other information.

What is the scoring system?

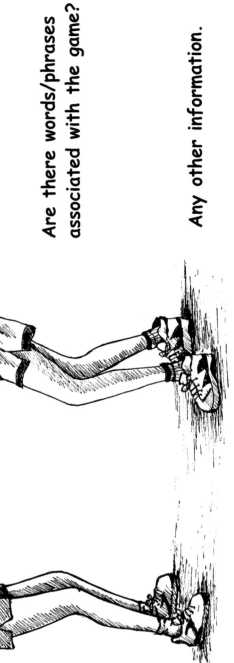

Basketball rules

Equipment needed
(make a list)

(use bullet points or numbers)

Number of players

Playing time

How to play (clear, sequenced instructions)

· ·

· ·

· ·

· ·

· ·

· ·

· ·

· ·

· ·

Safety point (important reminder)

· ·

· ·

· ·

(illustration)

Rules for_____

Choose another game to write the rules for.

(illustration)

[ ]

Equipment needed
(make a list)

Number of players

Playing time

How to play (clear, sequenced instructions)

(use bullet points or numbers)

. . . .

. . . .

. . . .

. . . .

. . . .

. . . .

. . . .

. . . .

. . . .

Safety point (important reminder)

. . . .

. . . .

. . . .

(illustration)

Unit 6 – Kangaroo and Koala

Learning objectives

- To write fables using structures/themes from reading (Term 2, T11).
- To develop characters suitable for a fable.
- To review and edit writing, matching to needs of audience (Term 2, T13).

Ideas for using the activity sheets

Page 31: Kangaroo and Koala

- Look at examples of fables. Make a class list of similarities in structure and themes. The children could use the list to help with completing the sheet. Scribe the beginning of the fable, keeping to the listed structure. The children could then work in pairs to complete the fable.
- Ask the children to use the completed sheet to write a news report about the incident. Can they think of a good headline? Tell them to include quotes from both animals involved, making sure that their comments give an insight into their character.
- Discuss the setting. What do we know about Australia? Collect adjectives to describe the landscape, climate and so on. Ask the children to write a start to the fable, describing the setting.

Page 32: Kangaroo and Koala conversation

- Look at the different characteristics of animals in fables. The children could work in small groups to make lists of words that could be used to describe both animals on the sheet. Share their ideas with the class. Discuss how these characteristics would determine how each animal would respond in a conversation. Ask the children to complete the sheet considering this.
- In pairs, each child could take on the role of one character. They could use role play to develop ideas for their conversation. Ask them to record their final ideas and perform the conversation to the class.
- Use completed sheets as part of a whole class composition. Model writing the beginning of the fable and discuss where the dialogue could be included. Ask the children to offer ideas from their sheets at appropriate points. Reread and edit the story as it develops. The children could complete the fable, adding dialogue to the story and reviewing their work as they write.

Page 33: Kangaroo and Koala story map

- Discuss writing in paragraphs. Ask the children to use their completed sheets to write a fable, set out in paragraphs. At given points, they could work with a partner, reviewing and editing their writing to improve it.
- Look at examples of stories written for a younger audience. Discuss what differences there are – list them. In pairs, the children could use their completed sheets to write a fable for a younger child. If possible, ask them to share the finished stories with a younger child and evaluate how successful it was.
- Ask them to use their completed plan to write a short play or pantomime. Discuss elements of a performance that they need to include. They could work in pairs, develop scenes, practise and perform it. Discuss areas of success and possible improvements.

Kangaroo and Koala

Make notes around the picture.

How did it start?

What are they doing?

Why are they doing it?

Why is Kangaroo in trouble?

What do you think of Kangaroo?

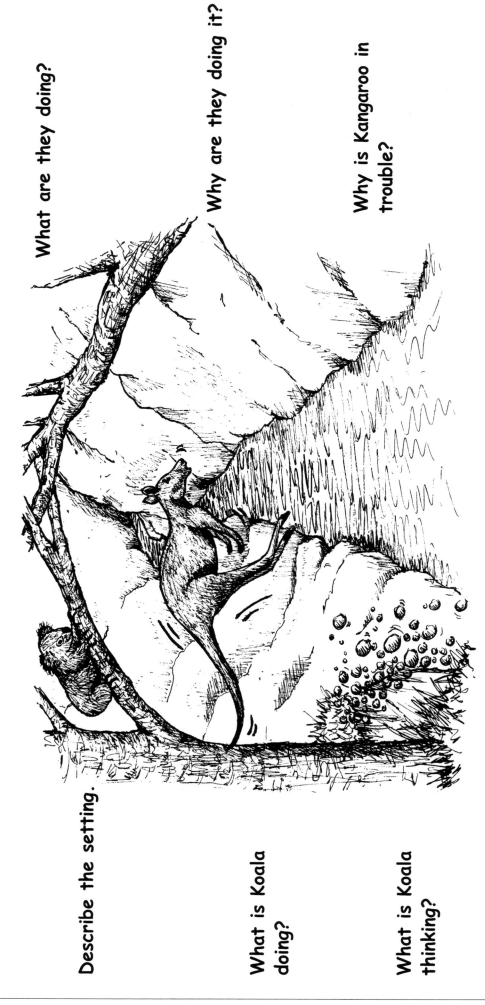

Where is it?

Describe the setting.

What is Koala doing?

What is Koala thinking?

What lesson will Kangaroo learn from this?

Kangaroo and Koala conversation

Write the conversation between the two characters.

 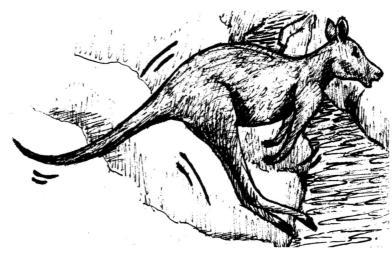

Koala   Kangaroo

(Introduce themselves to each other.)

....
....
....

(Say something about character/boast about what they can do.)

....
....
....

(Challenge to a competition/race.)

....
....
....

(Make a comment about how it turned out.)

....
....
....

Kangaroo and Koala
story map

Plan the key incidents of your fable.
Draw or write what will happen.

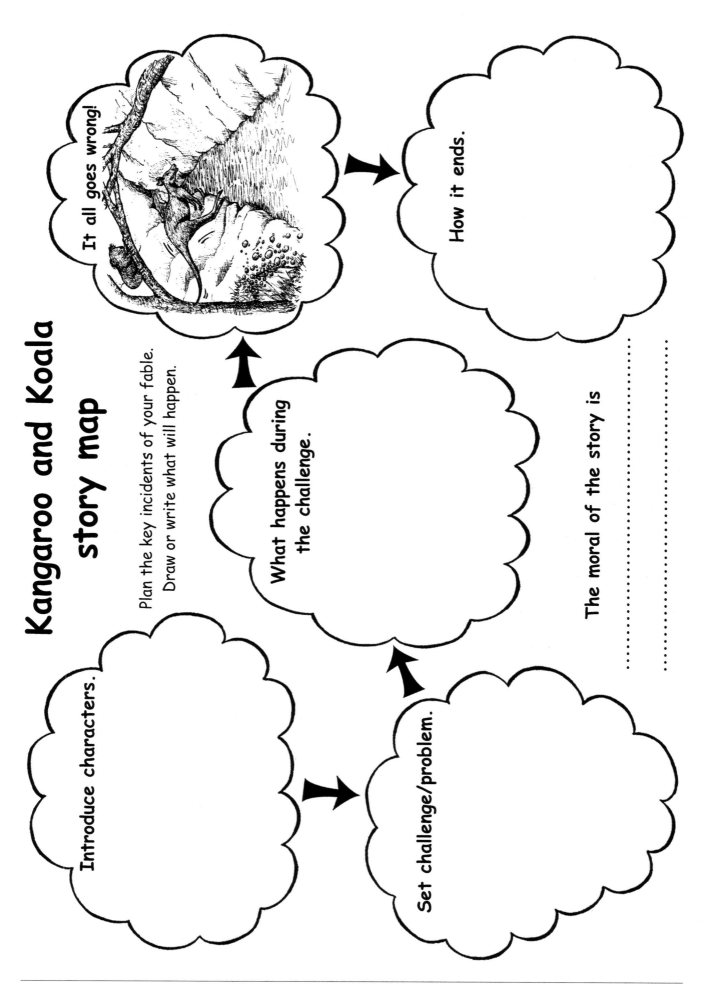

It all goes wrong!

How it ends.

What happens during the challenge.

The moral of the story is

....

Introduce characters.

Set challenge/problem.

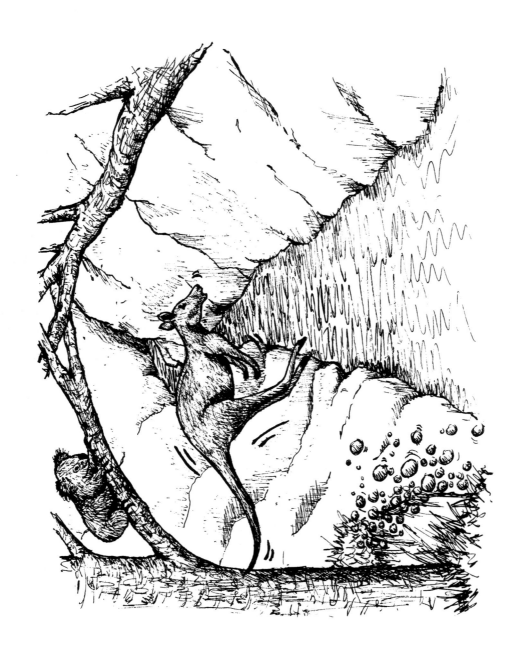

Unit 7 – The warrior's tale

Learning objectives

- To write legends and myths using structures/themes from reading (Term 2, T11).
- To describe characters/beasts from myths and legends (Term 2, T11).
- To write myths and legends based in a different culture (Term 2, T11).

Ideas for using the activity sheets

Page 36: The warrior's tale

- Collect stories involving dragons. Discuss the part they play in each tale. Is there a common theme? Are they stereotyped? Ask the children to complete the sheet with the dragon as a good character, and write the story as an alternative to the traditional style.
- Look at the common structure to myths and legends. Discuss similarities and differences. Make a class recipe for a traditional myth/legend. Ask the children to complete the sheet, using the recipe as guidance.
- Look at myths and legends from China and compare them with Western tales. Ask the children to consider these differences when completing the sheet.
- The children could write a letter from the warrior to a friend, retelling the incident.

Page 37: The dragon/the warrior

- The children could use ideas on the sheet to draw and describe their own mythical creature. They could write about a time when the warrior met the new creature. Make a class book telling of all the warrior's adventures and battles with the different beasts.
- Ask the children to use ideas from their completed sheets to write about when the warrior first came across the dragon. Act as a scribe for the children initially, writing down their ideas as well as demonstrating how reviewing and editing are important for improving a piece. The children could then complete the writing.
- They could write a paragraph about the battle scene between the two. They should use the completed sheet to help them decide what action each character will take and the outcome of the fight. Some of the class could write it from the warrior's point of view. Compare paragraphs written in 1st and 3rd person.

Page 38: The warrior's tale – story stages

- Look at the legend of George and the Dragon. Discuss how the story would change when retold in a different culture. Plot out the original version and ask the children to use this to retell the story from a Chinese perspective. (If available, look at stories from this culture to help.)
- Look at myths and legends from around the world. Choose a different culture, and ask the children to use the plan of story stages to rewrite it as if it happened there. Ask them to include places, phrases, weapons and so on that give the reader clues as to which country it is based in.
- Complete the sheet as an OHT with the whole class. Use the plan over three days, focusing on a different part each day. Build up a basic story as a class composition. Give the children copies of the story and ask them to improve it by adding more detail and description.

The warrior's tale

Make notes around the picture.

Describe the setting.

Who is he?

Describe him.

Why is he there?

How is he feeling?

Where is it?

When is it?

Describe the dragon.

What has the dragon done?

What will happen next?

Where does it live?   What does it do?   What sound does it make?

Does it smell?   What is its skin like?

What colour is it?   How does it move?

How does it attack?

The dragon

What does he look like?

The warrior

Describe his clothes.

Where does he live?   What sort of person is he?

Why is he fighting?

Has he any special powers?   How does he fight?

What weapons does he carry?

The warrior's tale - story stages

Make notes about what will happen at each stage of the story.

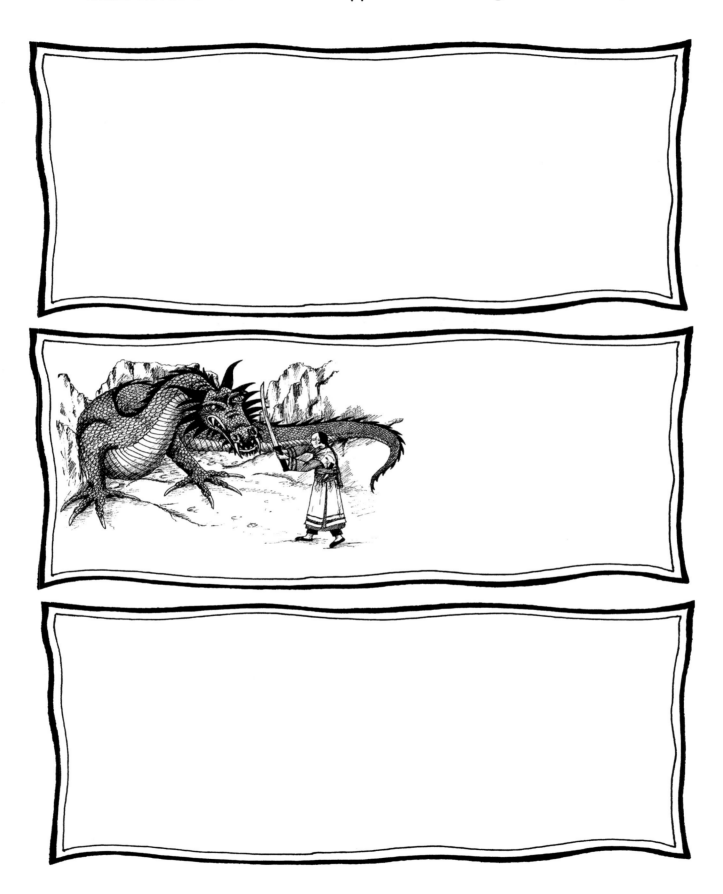

WRITING SPRINGBOARDS PHOTOCOPIABLE

Unit 8 – The strong boy

Learning objectives

- To write a narrative poem.
- To use structure of poems read to write own verses (Term 2, T12).
- To review and edit writing to produce final form (Term 2, T13).

Ideas for using the activity sheets

Page 41: The strong boy

- Look at examples of narrative poems. Discuss the similarities/differences in their composition and style. Complete the sheet as an OHT with the whole class. Discuss which poem style would best suit this story. Scribe the start of the poem in the agreed style and ask the children to work in pairs to complete it.
- Plan a sequence of events for a narrative poem as a class. Then ask the children to complete the sheet in pairs. They should use this information to write a poem, keeping to their planned sequence. Share the finished poems. Discuss the differences in the final pieces. Which parts were easiest/hardest to write?
- They could complete the sheet in small groups, using their ideas to write a group composition on large sheets of paper. After a given time, each group should pass their sheet to another group and spend time reviewing and improving the poem. Return the sheets to the original group to make any final adjustments. They could perform their poems and discuss the value of the reviewing process.

Page 42: Story of the strong boy

- Look at rhyming patterns in poems. Model writing the first verse (no rhyming pattern). Challenge the children to change the verse to fit in with different rhyming patterns. Share their ideas.
- Model writing a very basic poem on the sheet before the lesson. Ask the children to work on improving the poem by changing word order, adding interesting vocabulary, making it rhyme and so on.
- Give the children different parts of the poem to write. Working in small groups, they could bring the different parts together to form a whole poem. Ask them to edit verses where necessary, to form a complete narrative poem. Read it through and check the rhythm pattern. Share their poems with the class.

Page 43: Story of someone special

- Discuss possible talents or powers their character might have. Choose one, as a class, and work together, planning the story. They could use the plan to write individual poems about the character. Share their favourite parts at the end. Discuss the differences/similarities in how the plan has been interpreted.
- Make a list of super heroes and magical characters with special powers from books. Ask the children to write the poem about one of them without mentioning their name. Read the poems out to the class – can they guess who it is?
- The children could work in pairs, drawing their special character, and then writing the first verse of the poem. They then pass their sheet on to another pair to write the middle verse, and then on to a third pair to finish the poem. Return the sheets to the original pairs to edit and improve for the final version.

The strong boy

Make notes around the picture.

What is his name?

What is he doing?

Why is he doing it?

What does he look like?

What sort of person is he?

Where is it?

Describe the scene.

What has he done?

What will he do next?

What will stop him?

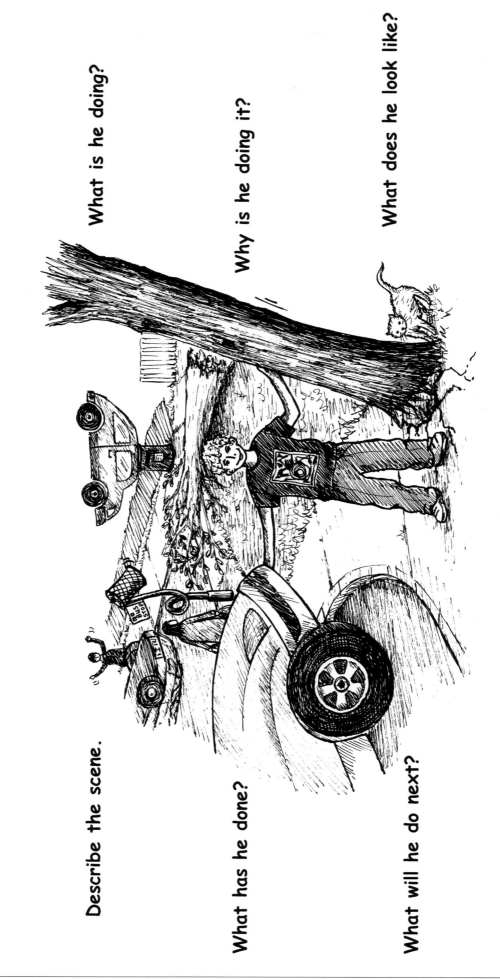

Story of the strong boy

Make a list of verbs you could
use in your poem.

Write his story as a poem.
Use the prompts to help you sequence your ideas.

....   **Who is he?**

....

....   **What is special about him?**

....   **How did it start?**

....   **What did he do?**

....   **When was it?**

....   **Where was it?**

....   **What did the people say?**

....   **How did they stop him?**

....   **What happened to him?**

Story of someone special

Make up your own character who is able to do something unusual.
Draw him/her doing it.

Write their story as a poem.
Use the prompts to help you sequence your ideas.

.... Who is it?

.... What is special about him/her?

....

.... How did it start?

What did he/she do?

....

.... When was it?

.... Where was it?

....

What did the people say?

....

.... How did they stop him/her?

.... What happened to him/her?

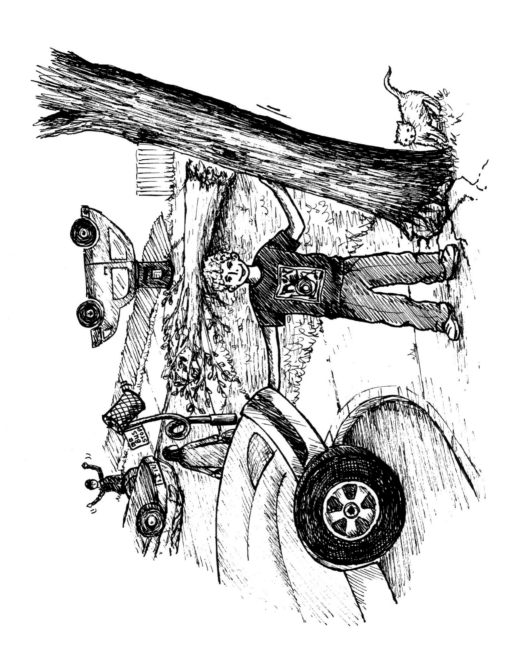

Unit 9 – The message

Learning objectives

- To write legends using structures/themes from reading (Term 2, T11).
- To describe characters from myths and legends.
- To review and edit writing, matching to needs of audience (Term 2, T13)

Ideas for using the activity sheets

Page 46: The message

- Look at examples of legends (if possible, different versions of the same one). As a class, decide on the common themes running through them. Ask the children to use this checklist when completing the sheet.
- Look at examples of medieval settings. List words to describe the setting. Complete the sheet as a whole class. The children could use this information to write a description of the scene, developing it into a description of what is happening at the point on the illustration.
- In small groups, the children could write a playscript scene based on the picture. They could use the answers on the sheet to help when planning the dialogue and stage directions. Perform the scenes.
- Discuss what the message might be, based on previous readings. Who is it from and why is it important? How will it move the story on? Ask the children to write the message, considering its importance to the story. They could experiment with calligraphy and try to make their message look authentic.

Page 47: The message – characters

- Discuss the importance of a hero in a legend and how their qualities can become exaggerated over time. In pairs, the children could list all the words/phrases to describe the knight. Share their ideas with the class, listing them on the board. They could go on to use these ideas to write a description of the knight. In a follow-up lesson, edit and review one pair's description (OHT). The children could then work on improving their own work.
- Ask the children to write a description of the knight from the point of view of the king or queen. What do they think of him? How will he be able to help them? Are they relying on him? Emphasise the need for the character's opinion to be obvious through the description.
- The children could use the completed sheet to write a conversation between the characters. Discuss how each character would be feeling and the effect this would have on what they say. Model how to set out dialogue correctly.

Page 48: The message story

- Discuss which aspects of legends the children like and why – wanting more action, interested in emotional aspects, comedy and so on. Decide on different audiences; for example, younger children. Working in pairs, the children could write a plan based on the needs of their selected audience. Share their plans with the class and discuss differences.
- Look at story structure of legends they have read. Make a class plan of the main events that are typical. Ask them to write their plan based on this structure and use the plan to write the story individually. Tell them that at each stage of the plan, they must stop and review their writing. When finished, discuss whether they kept to the original plan or made changes.

The message

Make notes around the picture.

When is it?

Where is it?

How is she feeling? Why?

What is he holding?

What does it say?

What will happen next?

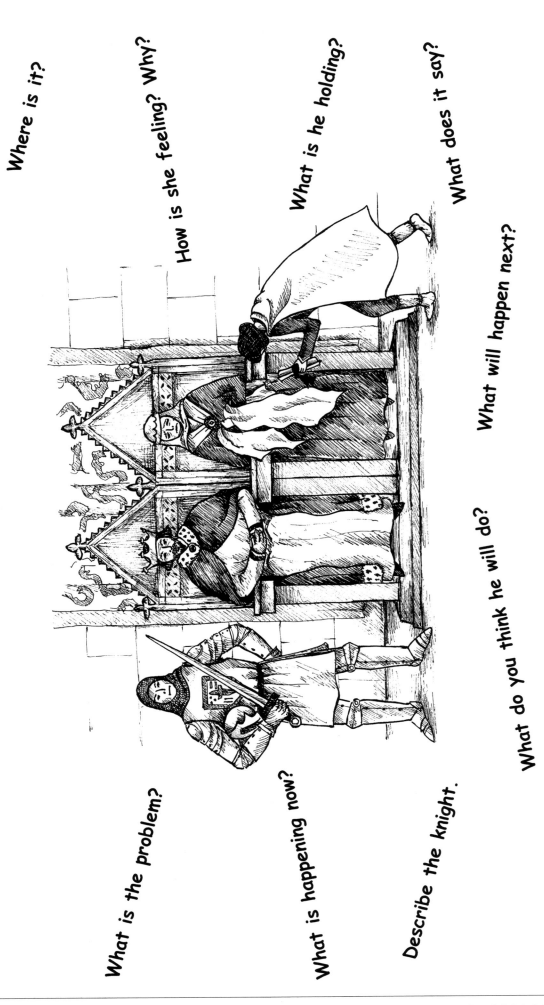

Who are they?

What is the problem?

What is happening now?

Describe the knight.

What do you think he will do?

WRITING SPRINGBOARDS

The message - characters

Describe his appearance.

Describe his character.

Give examples of his heroism.

Name:

What are they thinking or saying?

Choose either the king or queen and describe his/her character.

The message story

Map out the main events of the story.

Introduction

Ending

WRITING SPRINGBOARDS

Unit 10 – Switched on

Learning objectives

- To plan, compose, edit and refine explanatory texts (Term 2, T22).
- To use features of impersonal style; for example, technical vocabulary.
- To write a clear, concise explanation of a process.

Ideas for using the activity sheets

Page 51: Switched on

- Collect some advertisements and brochures about computer packages. Discuss how the information is displayed and what details they give. In pairs, the children could use their completed sheets to write a poster advertising the equipment. Tell them to include information about what each part does. Display their finished posters and evaluate them.
- Look at examples of diagrams/illustrations where labels have helped with understanding. Ask the children to label the equipment on the sheet and to write a brief explanation of what each part does.
- Complete the sheet on an OHT with the whole class. Focus on one part and make a list of the technical vocabulary you would use with it. Discuss where these terms might be explained. Make a glossary of the terms, and ask the children to write their own definitions.

Page 52: How to switch on

- Look at explanations of processes and collect words/phrases that make sequential, causal and logical connections (while, during, after, only when and so on). Ask the children to complete the sheet, using the listed phrases. Share their finished explanations, discussing clarity of sentences and use of listed words/phrases.
- Act as a scribe, modelling how to write a clear, concise explanatory text in an impersonal style. Discuss the different sections and what you would include in each. The children could then work in pairs, writing their own explanation for another part of the package.
- The children could use the school computers and make notes as they go through the process. They could use their notes to write their explanation. Ask them to swap completed sheets (or give them to another class) and follow the process, to operate the computer. Evaluate how easy they were to follow, clarity of sentences and so on.

Page 53: Switched on – Process plan

- The children could complete the sheet as homework, choosing an appliance from home and making notes on how it works. They could use this information to write a clear explanation with labelled diagrams.
- Demonstrate how to use a particular appliance, for example, a toaster. Ask the children to make notes on their sheets, as you go through the process. Act as a scribe, using their notes to write an explanation in full sentences. Work with the class to edit/refine the writing.
- Working in pairs, the children could make up an imaginary appliance; for example, a homework writer. They should discuss how it would work and make notes on the sheet. Can they make up technical words? They could then write up an explanation, including technical vocabulary and a glossary of terms. They could share their finished piece with other pairs.

Switched on

How does it work?

What is it connected to?

Technical vocabulary?

Make notes around the picture.

What is it called?

Does it use software/stationery?

What does it do?

How to switch on

Write an explanation of how one part of this package works.

<u>Introduction</u> (general information on how it fits in with rest of package)

. . . .

. . . .

. . . .

. . . .

. . . .

<u>How the</u> .... **<u>works</u>** (explain the process clearly and in order)

. . . .

. . . .

. . . .

. . . .

. . . .

. . . .

. . . .

. . . .

. . . .

. . . .

. . . .

<u>Conclusion</u> (make some closing statements about it)

. . . .

. . . .

. . . .

. . . .

Switched on – Process plan

Draw the appliance.

Plan your explanation of how it works.

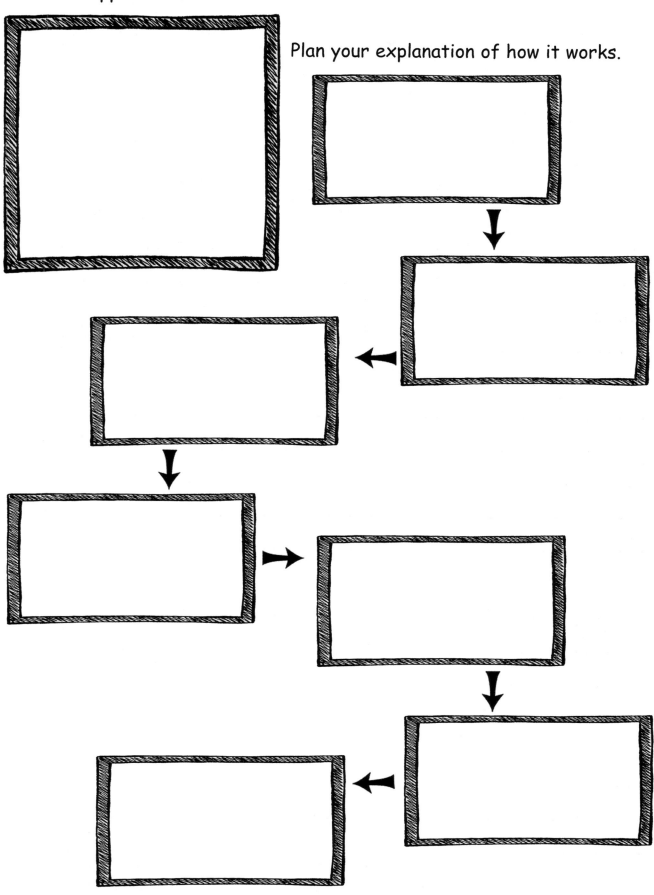

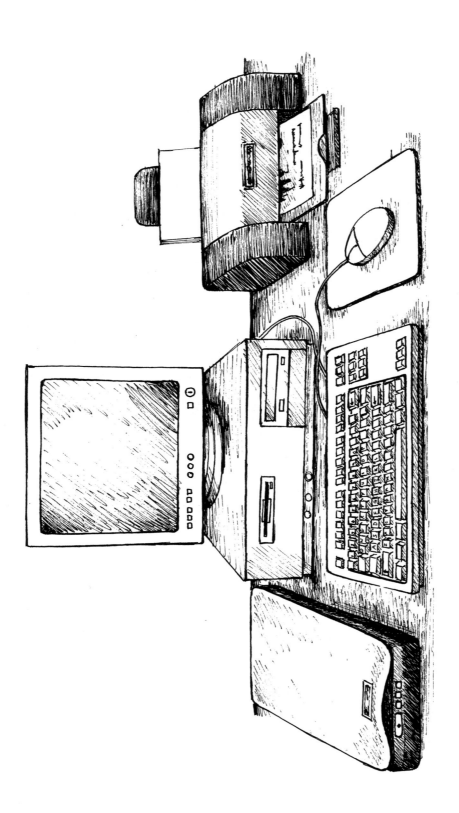

Unit 11 – The magic river

Learning objectives

- To write a story based in a different culture.
- To write from a different character's point of view (Term 3, T7).
- To predict what will happen in a story.

Ideas for using the activity sheets

Page 56: The magic river

- Look at the customs and lifestyle of an Indian village. Read stories from the culture. Ask the children to collect information to help them build up a realistic picture about life in India and ask them to use this to help them complete the sheet.
- The children could write about the girl's day leading up to the scene at the river. Decide, as a class, where she lives and with whom. What other jobs had she done that day? Write a plan for the first part of the story. The children could write the beginning of the story, stopping at the point illustrated. Share their ideas with the rest of the class.
- Look at examples of Indian sari fabrics. Discuss how decorative they are and how they could be described. The children could write a description of the fabric as it went into the river and the differences when it came out.

Page 57: The magic river – viewpoints

- Ask the children to choose one of the characters and write about a conversation that they had with a friend or family member when they reached home. They should include details about their feelings and how they interacted with the other character.
- Ask the children to work in pairs and each take on the role of a character. They should ask each other the questions on the sheet and record the responses. They could then use the answers to write the scene from their character's point of view.
- Tell the children to imagine that the scene is being watched from across the river. What sort of character could be watching them? Make a class list of possibilities. The children could write a description of what is happening from their point of view. Tell them to include their thoughts about the two characters, and also what they plan to do next. Share the finished ideas with the class.

Page 58: The magic river – prediction

- Act as a scribe, writing a paragraph about the scene illustrated. Review and edit the piece with the class. Look at the length of sentences – are there some that could be linked with connectives? Look at improving the vocabulary used and the order of ideas in the sentences. Plan the rest of the story together. The children could use the plan to continue the story to its conclusion. Encourage them to review their writing with an emphasis on the areas mentioned.
- In pairs, the children could come up with different predictions for the story. Share their ideas with the class and list them on the board. Discuss which are the most likely conclusions to the story, and why. The children could choose one of the ideas and write the rest of the story.
- Look at examples of stories written in the 1st person and the 3rd person. Discuss differences/similarities. Emphasise the importance of consistency. Ask the children to write the rest of the story from the point of view of one of the two characters. They need to decide whether to write it in the 1st or 3rd person.

The magic river

Make notes around the picture.

Where is it set?

When is it?

Who is she?

What sort of person is she?

Why is she down by the river?

How does she feel?

Who is he?

What is he doing?

What is he thinking?

What has happened to the fabric?

How has it happened?

What will she do?

The magic river - viewpoints

Think about how both characters would view the situation.

What does he think of the girl?

What can he see?

Did he have anything to do with it?

What is he thinking?

How does he feel?

What will he do?

What does she say?

What has happened?

Does she know the old man?

What does she think of him?

How does she react?

What is she going to do?

Does she know how it has happened?

The magic river - prediction

What do you think will happen next?
Plan the rest of the story.

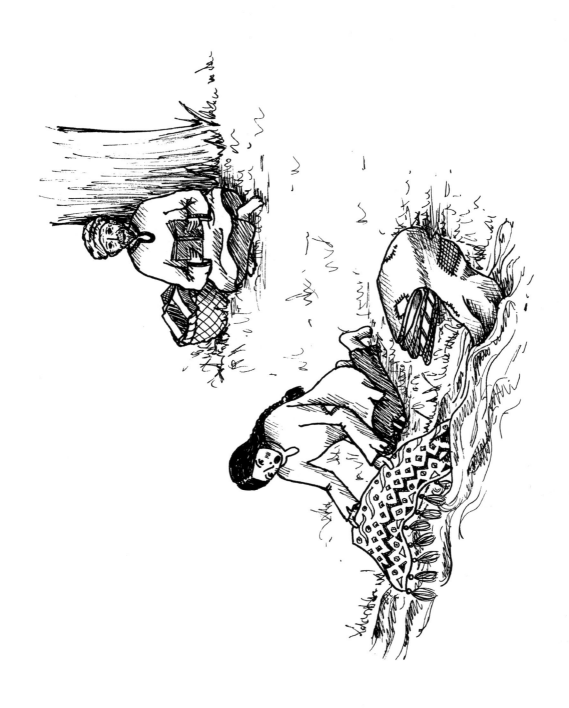

Unit 12 – The evacuees

Learning objectives

- To write from a character's point of view (Term 3, T7).
- To write stories from a different tradition.
- To consider attitudes, feelings, social customs of the time.

Ideas for using the activity sheets

Page 61: The evacuees

- Look at information about the Second World War. Discuss the ways in which life was different, and what happened when children were evacuated. Read examples from stories about that time. Ask the children to use this information to help them complete the sheet.
- The children could use the completed sheet to write a description of what is happening, from the mother's point of view. How is she feeling about everyone leaving? Where is she? How would she behave?
- Think about the atmosphere in the railway station with children leaving and soldiers going to the front line. Act as a scribe, writing a description of the setting. Include emotions and feelings so that the reader understands the attitudes of the time. Then ask the children to write their own version.

Page 62: The evacuees – characters

- The children could complete the sheet in pairs and then discuss how each character may have different views and feelings. They could write a conversation that one of the characters would have with a stranger on the train journey.
- Discuss how the characters would be feeling at this point. The children could work in pairs, each taking on the role of the father or a child. They could use their knowledge of the time, and the completed sheet, to help them develop an idea of what sort of character they are playing. They could then act out the scene and record the conversation (perhaps on tape?).
- Act as a scribe, using ideas from the sheet to write about the scene from the father's viewpoint. Ask the class to consider how they would feel if they were one of the children – discuss their feelings. The children could then individually write the same scene from the child's viewpoint.

Page 63: Letter from an evacuee

- Make a list of some of the differences to their normal lives the children would have experienced when they were evacuated. Use the sheet on an OHP, modelling the basic rules of letter writing. The children could then write a response to the letter from their friend who has also been evacuated.
- Discuss the experiences children had when they were evacuated – refer to extracts from stories about that time. Decide on some basic facts about the children's experiences (where they were, who they were with). The class could write letters home to their mothers, as if they had been evacuated.
- Look at the lifestyle of that time – food, entertainment, language and so on. Make a class list of items and phrases that were typical of that period. The children could work in pairs, writing the letter, including some of the ideas listed, to reflect that time. Share the finished letters – who has been most successful?

The evacuees

Make notes around the picture.

Give each character a name.

Where is he going?

Where are the children going?

How are they feeling? Why?

What sort of father is he?

What will happen next?

Who else would be there?

What sounds would there be?

When is it?

Where is it set?

The evacuees - characters

Answer the questions from the viewpoint of the character.

What do you think of the war?

What is your name?

When will you see your children again?

Where are you going?

Who will cope with the changes?   What do you think of your children?

What will you say to them?

The father

How do you feel?

His child

What is your name?

How old are you?

What do you think of your siblings?

What do you think of your father?

How do you feel about being evacuated?

What will you miss most?

What do you think of the war?

How will you say goodbye?

Letter from an evacuee

Write your letter as if you were one of the children who have been evacuated.

address evacuated to ➡

date ➡

greeting ↘

(Introduction - ask how they are, tell them why you're writing, give your location.)

....

....

....

(Main part - what the people are like, differences with home, how your siblings
are coping, what you miss, how you feel.)

....

....

....

....

....

....

....

(Ending - hope to see them soon, ask them to write back.)

....

....

⬅ closure

WRITING SPRINGBOARDS

Unit 13 – The street

Learning objectives

- To write performance poetry (Term 3, T11).
- To use different styles/structures in the poem.
- To revise, redraft and present a performance poem (Term 3, T11).

Ideas for using the activity sheets

Page 66: The street

- Look at different examples of performance poetry. Make a list of different structures and styles that are commonly used. Keep the list displayed as a checklist for the class. Complete the sheet as a class, then ask different groups of children to focus on one particular style/structure and to write a verse for the poem. Share their ideas.
- Make a list of all the things that could be written about in the poem on the street. Include ideas not featured on the illustration. Ask the children to work in small groups to record their ideas for one particular area and then make a verse out of their ideas. They could then perform it to the class.
- Look at rhyming patterns in poetry. The children could complete the sheet in pairs, trying to find words that rhyme. They then use the completed sheet to write sets of rhyming couplets. Share their ideas and compose a performance poem as a whole class.

Page 67: Sounds of the street

- For homework, ask the children to listen to street sounds and list what they hear. Tape record sounds on local streets at different times. Play the recordings and discuss the sounds. Make a list of all the sounds they have heard. The children could then use the ideas to write their poems.
- Scribe the first verse, considering some of the styles mentioned. Work with the class, revising and trying out different ideas. Ask the children to work in pairs to come up with a suitable middle verse, trying it out with the first verse to check for continuity in style. The class could work together on the final verse, then the children could work in their pairs revising the last verse to complete the performance.
- Discuss the use of onomatopoeia in poetry. Make a list of words that could be used in their poem. The children could work in pairs, writing a poem using the onomatopoeic words.

Page 68: My street

- Discuss the different times of day on a street. List the stages and discuss how they differ (quieter, busier, noisier and so on). Decide how these changes can be shown in their poem (speed, volume and silences). The children could work on verses to represent the different times. Ask them to perform their poems and share ideas about the most successful parts.
- Look at the use of similes and metaphors in poetry to evoke a mood. Discuss how a driver might feel in a traffic jam when they are late for an appointment. Ask the children to use their ideas about mood and the problems people face to write a poem that includes similes or metaphors.
- Work on a whole class composition about the street outside the school. Plan the stages through a school day and develop a performance poem for the whole class to be involved in (you act as scribe). Perform the poem to the school in an assembly.

The street

Make notes around the picture.

Sounds

Smells

Movements

Names

Colours

Shapes

Feelings

People

Sounds of the street

Make a list of all the sounds you
would hear on a busy street.

Write a performance poem about the sounds.

Think about:

Rhyme

Rhyming pattern

Sound effects

Rhythm

Actions

Alliteration

Chorus

Order of words

Volume

Vocabulary

Similes

Metaphors

....

....

....

....

....

....

....

....

....

....

....

....

Names   Smells   # My street   Colours   Feelings

Movements   Sounds   Shapes   People

Draw a picture of your street. Make notes around it.

Write a performance poem about the sounds.   **Think about:**

....   **Rhyme**

....   **Patterns**

....   **Rhythm**

....

....   **Alliteration**

....   **Metaphors**

....   **Similes**

....   **Chorus**

....   **Interesting
vocabulary**

....

....   **Performance**

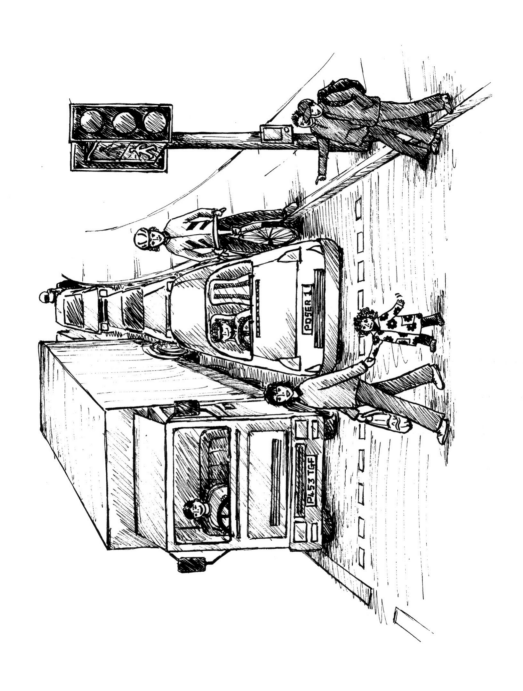

Unit 14 – The storm

Learning objectives

- To write a story based in a different culture.
- To write from a different character's point of view (Term 3, T7).
- To plan the key events in a story.

Ideas for using the activity sheets

Page 71: The storm

- Look at examples of stories where storms are involved. Make a list of adjectives used in the descriptions of the storms. Ask the children to use the completed sheet and the list to write a description of the scene. Read them out and evaluate how successful they have been in building up an atmosphere.
- Research fishing in African countries. Look at methods used, and lifestyles connected the occupation. Ask the children to use this information to help them complete the sheet, considering the culture in which it is set. Share their ideas and comment on who has been sympathetic to the cultures and traditions.
- Ask the children to predict what will happen next and list all the possibilities. Tell them to think about stories they have read that follow a similar theme – how did they progress? Scribe the story for the scene shown, using questions on the sheet as prompts. The children could choose one of the listed predictions and continue the story individually.

Page 72: The storm – dialogue

- Listen to taped stories and radio dramas. Ask the children to work in small groups, developing a conversation between the characters as part of a radio drama. Discuss the importance of clear, expressive speech and sound effects. They could record the drama on tape and replay it to the class.
- Discuss how the two characters would have different personalities and therefore react in a different way. This would have had an effect on how they interacted with each other. Act as a scribe, modelling how the dialogue should be set out and varying the order of sentences. Ask the children to offer ideas for dialogue for each character. They could then work individually to complete the conversation.
- Discuss the different points of view from which the story could be told (narrator, one of the boys, another character). How would this affect the perspective and therefore how the conversation is written? Ask different groups to write the conversation from a certain viewpoint. Compare results.

Page 73: The storm – story plan

- The children could use the story plan to write the story as a diary page. Look at examples of stories written in this way. List the common structures. The children need to decide which character they are writing for.
- Tell the children to imagine that the boys sent a message for help in a bottle. What would it say? What information would they give? Ask the children to write that message.
- Look at how connectives are used to link clauses within sentences. Make a list of connectives. Develop the start of the story as a whole class with you acting as scribe, including connectives where appropriate. The children could complete the story.

The storm

Make notes around the picture.

Where is it set?

Where do they live?

Describe the weather.

What are they doing?

What is the problem?

Who are they?

Are they related?

What are they like?

How are they feeling?

What will happen next?

The storm - dialogue

What are their names?

Are they friends?

Who is most scared?

Who will take charge?

What is the problem?

How are they feeling?

Is it someone's fault?

Do they agree about what they should do?

Consider the situation that the two boys find themselves in.

Write the conversation they might have.

....

....

....

....

....

....

....

....

....

....

....

....

The storm - story plan

Plan out the key events in your story.

Where did it start?

How was it going?

Why did they go fishing?

Who noticed that the weather had changed?

Are they rescued?

How does it end?

Do they survive the storm?

Unit 15 – Spoilt sea

Learning objectives

- To write a commentary on an issue presented as a leaflet (Term 3, T18).
- To write a letter on an issue (Term 3, T17).
- To construct an argument to persuade others of a point of view (Term 3, T19).

Ideas for using the activity sheets

Page 76: Spoilt sea

- Collect information on sea/beach pollution. Use the internet to find relevant sites. Discuss the issue in terms of worldwide and national problems. Make a class display of information. In pairs, the children could complete the sheet and design posters for the display.
- Make a class list of all the activities people do at the seaside. Discuss which have a damaging effect on the environment and how this can be prevented. The children could complete the sheet in pairs and use the information to write a short talk on how to look after the beach environment. After they have presented their talks, discuss which parts were effective and the language used.
- Invite a representative from an environmental charity/organisation to give a talk to the class about issues related to sea pollution. Use the sheet to generate questions.

Page 77: Spoilt sea leaflet

- Look at examples of leaflets/newspaper articles on particular issues. Locate and discuss persuasive devices used. Ask the children to make note on issues to raise. Model how to write the sentences in a persuasive way. The children can complete the sheet individually.
- Scribe the issues raised. Work on editing and improving the argument. Is it effective? Are there better phrases/words? Ask the children to work in pairs to develop catchy titles and final messages. Share these with the class and discuss which are the most catchy and which put across the message clearly.
- Ask the children to design and write a follow-up leaflet written by the company responsible for the tanker transporting oil. Can they write an argument for this form of transportation?

Page 78: Spoilt sea letter

- Make a class list of organisations you could send a letter to regarding sea pollution. Discuss how some would be letters of complaint (newspapers, councils and so on) and others would be letters of support (charities, support groups). How would the tone of the letters differ? Ask the children to write their letters to a particular organisation. Share the final letters – can they tell who they have been written to (a charity or a council for example)?
- Ask the children to choose another environmental issue (perhaps to do with a local issue). Ask them to write a letter putting their point of view. If applicable, send the letters to a relevant organisation. Review any responses. Display the responses for all the class to read.
- Ask the children to swap letters and write the reply they would expect to receive. Discuss the need for them to respond to the issues raised in a formal and polite manner. They could evaluate the letters in pairs.

Spoilt sea

Label all the problems you can see.
Write down what they do to the sea and who/what they affect.

Can you think of anything else which damages the sea?

Spoilt sea leaflet

(catchy title)

(points to raise)

....

....

....

....

....

....

(final message)

Spoilt sea letter

Imagine that you are one of the people in the attached photo. Write a letter to a newspaper putting forward your point of view.

[   ]

[   ]

(formal greeting)

[   ]

(why you are writing)

....

....

....

(your arguments)

....

....

....

....

....

....

(final comments, plan of action)

....

....

....

[   ]

(formal closure)

Response partners

Review your writing and then
ask a friend to do the same.
Write the comments in the speech bubbles.

What is the
best part?

Which is your
favourite character?

Which is your
favourite line or
sentence?

How could it be
made better?

Self-assessment
How do you think you have done?

very good   OK   not so good

Writing activity:

Planning:

Writing style:

Layout:

Punctuation:

Special vocabulary:

Spelling:

Editing/redrafting:

Final published presentation:

Other comments:

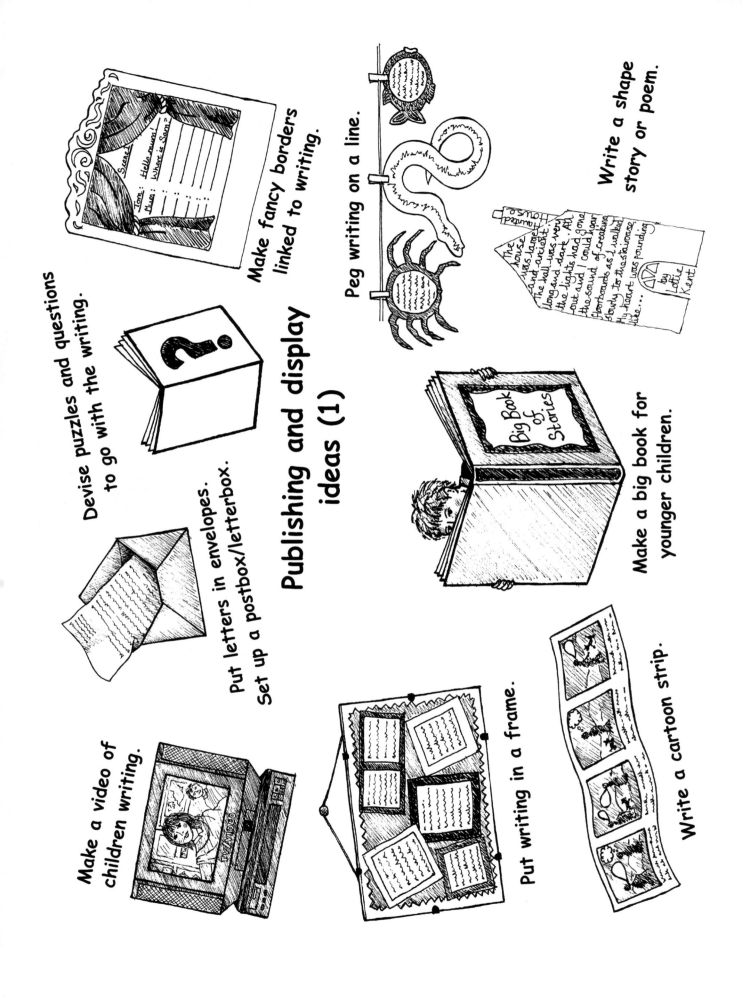

Make fancy borders linked to writing.

Peg writing on a line.

Write a shape story or poem.

Devise puzzles and questions to go with the writing.

Put letters in envelopes. Set up a postbox/letterbox.

Publishing and display ideas (1)

Make a big book for younger children.

Big Book of Stories

Make a video of children writing.

Put writing in a frame.

Write a cartoon strip.

Make a newspaper or magazine.

Put the writing on a 3-D shape.

Put writing on a wall mural.

HAUNTED HOUSE

Experiment with font style and layout on the computer.

THE LOST ISLAND

Make an environment to display/contain the writing.

Publishing and display ideas (2)

Put the words to a well known tune.

Make scrolls.

The Hunter
In the dark, mysterious jungle, the hunter sat as still as...

Make a book with moving parts.

Put it on tape.

Writing targets

Three things I need to work on:

Writing targets

Three things I need to work on: